FIRST FORM LATIN

QUIZZES AND TESTS

Cheryl Lowe

First Form Latin

Quizzes and Tests
by Cheryl Lowe

Published by:
Memoria Press
www.memoriapress.com

First Edition © 2009 by Memoria Press 0317
ISBN # 978-1-61538-006-0

Vocabulary:

I call	_____	I prepare	_____
I carry	_____	I speak, pray	_____
I give	_____	I stand	_____
I guard, keep	_____	I swim	_____
I love, like	_____	I wash	_____

Latin Saying:

Let us recite together _____

A. Conjugate *porto* in the present tense with meanings:

Person	Singular	Meaning	Plural	Meaning
1st				
2nd				
3rd				

B. Translate from Latin to English:

1. das _____

2. stamus _____

3. servant _____

C. Translate from English to Latin:

1. he gives _____

2. I love _____

3. they carry _____

D. Fill in the table with the English pronouns and Latin personal endings.

Person	English Pronoun (s.)	English Pronoun (pl.)	Latin Ending (s.)	Latin Ending (pl.)
1st				
2nd				
3rd				

Bonus:

Give an example in English of: the simple present _____

the progressive present _____

the emphatic present _____

Vocabulary:

I call	_____	I plow	_____
I carry	_____	I praise	_____
I desire, wish	_____	I prepare	_____
I err, wander	_____	I shout	_____
I fight	_____	I speak, pray	_____
I give	_____	I stand	_____
I guard, keep	_____	I swim	_____
I help	_____	I tell	_____
I look at	_____	I tempt	_____
I love, like	_____	I wash	_____

Latin Saying:

The Mother was Standing _____

A. Conjugate *clamo* in the present and imperfect tenses:

Person	Present		Imperfect	
1st				
2nd				
3rd				

B. Translate from Latin to English:

1. pugnabatis _____
2. optabant _____
3. laudabat _____
4. clamabamus _____

C. Translate from English to Latin:

1. they were telling _____
2. I was looking at _____
3. you were praising _____
4. we were wandering _____

Bonus:

The imperfect tense is translated into English by the helping verbs _____ and _____.

What is the minimum number of words required to make a Latin sentence? _____

Vocabulary:

I adore	_____	I plow	_____
I call	_____	I praise	_____
I carry	_____	I prepare	_____
I desire, wish	_____	I sail	_____
I err, wander	_____	I seize	_____
I fight	_____	I set free	_____
I give	_____	I shout	_____
I greet	_____	I speak, pray	_____
I guard, keep	_____	I stand	_____
I help	_____	I swim	_____
I judge, consider	_____	I tell	_____
I live in, dwell	_____	I tempt	_____
I look at	_____	I walk	_____
I love, like	_____	I wash	_____
I overcome, surpass	_____	I work	_____

Latin Saying:

Then we will fight in the shade. _____

A. Match the correct label with the part of the word it belongs with.

a. personal pronoun ending

b. stem

voca ba t   c. tense sign
 ___   ___ ___

B. Translate from Latin to English:

1. laborabit _____

2. navigabo _____

3. judicabimus _____

4. salutabunt _____

C. Translate from English to Latin:

1. they will seize _____

2. you will adore _____

3. we will overcome _____

4. they will dwell _____

D. Conjugate *laboro*:

present:

	Singular	Plural
1st		
2nd		
3rd		

imperfect:

	Singular	Plural
1st		
2nd		
3rd		

future:

	Singular	Plural
1st		
2nd		
3rd		

E. Grammar Questions:

1. The imperfect tense is translated into English by the helping verbs _____ and _____ .

2. The future tense is translated into English by the helping verb _____ .

3. The tense sign for the imperfect tense is _____ .

4. The tense sign for the future tense is _____ .

5. In Latin grammar **imperfect** means _____ .

Bonus:

1. Latin is a language of _____ and _____ .

A. Choose the correct answer from the list below to answer questions 1-5:

to love   infinitive   stems   principal parts   are

1. The four main forms for each verb are called the verb's _____ .

2. These forms provide the _____ needed to conjugate each verb in all its tenses.

3. The second principal part is the _____ .

4. The second principal part of every 1st conjugation verb ends in _____ .

5. The infinitive of amo (amare) means _____ .

B. Answer the following questions:

1. How do you find the present stem for a Latin verb? _____

    _____

2. Name the 3 tenses (in order) that make up the Present System. _____

    _____

3. What are the first 2 principal parts of *do*? _____

4. What are the first 2 principal parts of *oro*? _____

5. What is the infinitive of *narro*? _____

C. Conjugate *lavo* in the future:

	Singular	Plural
1st		
2nd		
3rd		

D. Conjugate *júdico* in the present:

	Singular	Plural
1st		
2nd		
3rd		

E. Conjugate *óccupo* **in the imperfect:**

	Singular	Plural
1st		
2nd		
3rd		

F. Answer the following:

1. Using the verb **arabatis**, answer the following questions:

   What is the stem? _____ What is the tense sign? _____

   What is the personal pronoun ending? _____

2. The helping verbs used with the imperfect tense are _____ and _____ .

3. The helping verb used with the future tense is _____ .

G. Translate:

1. spectabunt _____

2. ambulabat _____

3. servas _____

4. parabit _____

Bonus:

   Translate:

1. Stabat Mater _____

2. In umbra, ígitur, pugnábimus. _____

Latin Saying:

I am a Roman citizen. _____

A. Conjugate *sum* in the present, imperfect, and future tenses:

Person	Present		Imperfect	
1st				
2nd				
3rd				

Person	Future	
1st		
2nd		
3rd		

B. Answer the following:

1. The verb *sum* shows existence, not_____ .

2. Give the infinitive of *sum*: _____

C. Translate from Latin to English:

1. erimus _____

2. erat _____

3. estis _____

4. erunt _____

5. sumus _____

6. eram _____

D. Translate from English to Latin:

1. they are _____

2. I will be _____

3. she was _____

4. you (pl.) were _____

5. you will be _____

6. he is _____

Bonus:

1. Are the personal endings of *sum* regular or irregular? _____

2. Is the infinitive of *sum* regular or irregular? _____

Conjugate *amo* in the present, imperfect, and future tenses:

Person	Present		Imperfect	
1st				
2nd				
3rd				

Person	Future	
1st		
2nd		
3rd		

Conjugate *do* in the present, imperfect, and future tenses:

Person	Present		Imperfect	
1st				
2nd				
3rd				

Person	Future	
1st		
2nd		
3rd		

Conjugate *sum* in the present, imperfect, and future tenses:

Person	Present		Imperfect	
1st				
2nd				
3rd				

Person	Future	
1st		
2nd		
3rd		

Vocabulary: Give the infinitive form for each Latin verb.

to adore	_____	to plow	_____
to call	_____	to praise	_____
to carry	_____	to prepare	_____
to desire, wish	_____	to sail	_____
to err, wander	_____	to seize	_____
to fight	_____	to set free	_____
to give	_____	to shout	_____
to greet	_____	to speak, pray	_____
to guard, keep	_____	to stand	_____
to help	_____	to swim	_____
to judge, consider	_____	to tell	_____
to live in, dwell	_____	to tempt	_____
to look at	_____	to walk	_____
to love, like	_____	to wash	_____
to overcome, surpass	_____	to work	_____

Grammar and Latin Sayings:

1. Verb families are called_____ .

2. Give the 6 attributes of a Latin verb._____

   _____

3. Give the three grammar persons. _____

4. Give the two grammar numbers. _____

5. The stem vowel of the 1st conjugation is _____ .

6. In English, *I praise* is the _____ present, *I am praising* is the _____ present,

   and *I do praise* is the _____ present.

7. The imperfect tense sign is _____ .

8. What English helping verbs translate the imperfect tense? _____

9. How many words are needed to make a Latin sentence?_____

10. The future tense sign is _____ .

11. What English helping verb translates the Latin future tense? _____

12. Name the 3 tenses that make up the Present System. _____

    _____

13. The forms that provide the stems needed to conjugate a verb in all its tenses are called the

    _____   _____ .

14. Give the infinitive of sum. _____

15. A verb whose infinitive ends in _____ belongs to the 1st conjugation.

16. What is the name of the 2nd principal part? _____

17. How do you find the present stem? _____

18. The English infinitive is written with the particle _____ before the verb.

19. The 'to be' verb shows _____ , not action.

20. Give the English forms of the 'to be' verb. _____

    _____

21. In choro recitémus. _____

22. Civis Romanus sum. _____

23. Stabat Mater _____

24. In umbra, ígitur, pugnábimus _____

Latin Saying:

Errare est humanum. _____

A. Give the principal parts for the following verbs:

1st	2nd	3rd	4th
clamo			
porto			
do			
specto			
pugno			
ámbulo			
lavo			
sto			
óccupo			
narro			
saluto			

B. Translate:

1. We were preparing to sail. _____

2. You like to walk. _____

3. They desire to work. _____

4. Opto juvare. _____

5. Parabit pugnare. _____

6. Amatis arare. _____

Bonus:

1. How do you find the present stem of a Latin verb? _____

_____

Vocabulary:

then, at that time	_____	never	_____
ever	_____	today	_____
often	_____	always	_____
not	_____	tomorrow	_____
yesterday	_____	now	_____

Latin Saying:

now or never _____

A. Answer the following:

1. To find the stem of a Present System verb, you drop the _____ from the _____ .

2. To find the stem of a Perfect System verb, you drop the _____ from the _____ .

B. Give the perfect stem of the following verbs:

1. servo _____

2. laudo _____

3. occupo _____

4. do _____

5. sto _____

6. lavo _____

7. juvo _____

8. ambulo _____

C. Give the perfect tense personal endings:

Person	Singular	Plural
1st		
2nd		
3rd		

D. Conjugate *pugno* in the perfect tense with meanings:

Person	Singular	Meaning	Plural	Meaning
1st				
2nd				
3rd				

E. Conjugate *sto* in the perfect tense with meanings:

Person	Singular	Meaning	Plural	Meaning
1st				
2nd				
3rd				

F. Translate from Latin to English:

1. laboravimus _____
2. dedisti _____
3. salutaverunt _____
4. paravit _____
5. judicavi _____
6. navigavisti _____

G. Translate from English to Latin:

1. I have seized _____
2. it has carried _____
3. they have shouted _____
4. you (pl.) have fought _____
5. you have stood _____
6. we have helped _____

Bonus:
Translate:

1. I have never plowed_____
2. she has not prepared _____
3. yesterday they fought _____

Name_____ Date _____

Vocabulary: Give the infinitive form for each Latin verb.

to doubt   _____   to hide   _____

to change   _____   to hope   _____

to accuse   _____   to disturb   _____

to think   _____   to deny   _____

to ask   _____   to fly   _____

Latin Saying:

always faithful _____

A. Give the pluperfect tense endings:

Person	Singular	Plural
1st		
2nd		
3rd		

B. Answer the following:

1. The pluperfect tense endings are identical to the _____ tense of *sum*.

2. The pluperfect tense is translated into English using the helping verb _____ .

C. Conjugate *rogo* in the pluperfect tense:

Person	Singular	Meaning	Plural	Meaning
1st				
2nd				
3rd				

D. Conjugate *puto* in the perfect and pluperfect tenses:

Person	Perfect		Pluperfect	
1st				
2nd				
3rd				

E. Conjugate *do* in the perfect and pluperfect tenses:

Person	Perfect		Pluperfect	
1st				
2nd				
3rd				

F. Translate from Latin to English:

1. volaverat _____
2. putaveram _____
3. accusaverant _____
4. negaveramus _____
5. speraveras _____
6. rogaveratis _____

G. Translate from English to Latin:

1. we had asked _____
2. she had hidden _____
3. you had changed _____
4. you (pl.) had thought _____
5. they had flown _____
6. I had doubted _____

Bonus:

1. To err is human. _____
2. Then we will fight in the shade. _____

Vocabulary: Give the infinitive form for each Latin verb.

to address	_____	to ask	_____
to wait for, expect	_____	to attack	_____
to doubt	_____	to hide	_____
to show, point out	_____	to explore	_____
to change	_____	to create	_____
to blame	_____	to hope	_____
to wound	_____	to disturb	_____
to accuse	_____	to deny	_____
to think	_____	to delight, please	_____
to report	_____	to fly	_____

Latin Saying:

Fortune aids the brave. _____

A. Give the future perfect tense personal endings:

Person	Singular	Plural
1st		
2nd		
3rd		

B. Answer the following

1. The English helping verbs needed to translate the Latin future perfect tense are _____ and _____ .

2. The future perfect tense endings are **almost** the same as the _____ tense of *sum*.

C. Conjugate *culpo* in the future perfect tense:

P	Singular	Meaning	Plural	Meaning
1st				
2nd				
3rd				

D. Conjugate *exploro* in the perfect, pluperfect, and future perfect tenses:

Person	Perfect		Pluperfect	
1st				
2nd				
3rd				

Person	Future Perfect	
1st		
2nd		
3rd		

E. Translate from Latin to English:

1. vulneráverit _____

2. nuntiáverint _____

3. appellávero _____

4. oppugnavéritis _____

5. delectavérimus _____

6. culpáveris _____

F. Translate from English to Latin:

1. they will have created _____

2. I will have shown _____

3. he will have attacked _____

4. you (pl.) will have explored _____

5. we will have blamed _____

6. you will have wounded _____

Bonus:

1. Name the six attributes of a verb: _____

Latin Saying:

Pray and work. _____

A. Conjugate *sum* in the perfect, pluperfect, and future perfect tenses:

Person	Perfect		Pluperfect	
1st				
2nd				
3rd				

Person	Future Perfect	
1st		
2nd		
3rd		

B. Translate from Latin to English:

1. fuerunt _____

2. fúeram _____

3. fuéritis _____

4. fúimus _____

5. fúerant _____

C. Translate from English to Latin:

1. you will have been _____

2. she has been _____

3. he had been _____

4. we will have been _____

5. I have been _____

Bonus:

1. Give the principal parts of *sum*: _____

Name_____ Date _____

First Form Latin Test: Unit II, Lesson 12 *page 1*

Vocabulary: Give the infinitive form for each Latin verb.

to address _____	to ask _____
to wait for, expect _____	to attack _____
to doubt _____	to hide _____
to show, point out _____	to explore _____
to change _____	to create _____
to blame _____	to hope _____
to wound _____	to disturb _____
to accuse _____	to deny _____
to think _____	to delight, please _____
to report _____	to fly _____
then, at that time _____	never _____
ever _____	today _____
often _____	always _____
not _____	tomorrow _____
yesterday _____	now _____

Grammar:

1. Give the principal parts of *sum*._____

   do _____

   sto _____

   lavo _____

   juvo _____

2. Give 3 translations for *vocavi*._____

   _____

Latin Sayings:

1. To err is human._____

2. always faithful _____

3. Pray and work._____

4. now or never _____

5. Fortune aids the brave. _____

Conjugations:

A. Conjugate *celo* in the perfect, pluperfect, and future perfect tenses:

P	Perfect		Pluperfect	
1st				
2nd				
3rd				

P	Future Perfect	
1st		
2nd		
3rd		

B. Give meanings for *celo* in the perfect, pluperfect, and future perfect tenses:

P	Perfect		Pluperfect	
1st				
2nd				
3rd				

P	Future Perfect	
1st		
2nd		
3rd		

Conjugations:

C. Conjugate *sum* in the perfect, pluperfect, and future perfect tenses:

P	Perfect		Pluperfect	
1st				
2nd				
3rd				

P	Future Perfect	
1st		
2nd		
3rd		

D. Give meanings for *sum* in the perfect, pluperfect, and future perfect tenses:

P	Perfect		Pluperfect	
1st				
2nd				
3rd				

P	Future Perfect	
1st		
2nd		
3rd		

Conjugate *muto* in the present, imperfect, and future tenses:

Person	Present		Imperfect	
1st				
2nd				
3rd				

Person	Future	
1st		
2nd		
3rd		

Conjugate *do* in the perfect, pluperfect, and future perfect tenses:

Person	Perfect		Pluperfect	
1st				
2nd				
3rd				

Person	Future Perfect	
1st		
2nd		
3rd		

Conjugate *sum* in the present, imperfect, and future tenses:

Person	Present		Imperfect	
1st				
2nd				
3rd				

Person	Future	
1st		
2nd		
3rd		

Conjugate *sum* in the perfect, pluperfect, and future perfect tenses:

Person	Perfect		Pluperfect	
1st				
2nd				
3rd				

Person	Future Perfect	
1st		
2nd		
3rd		

Give Meanings:

accuso		hábito		paro	
adoro		júdico		perturbo	
ámbulo		juvo		porto	
amo		laboro		pugno	
appello		laudo		puto	
aro		lavo		rogo	
celo		líbero		saluto	
clamo		muto		servo	
creo		narro		specto	
culpo		nato		spero	
delecto		návigo		sto	
demonstro		nego		súpero	
do		núntio		tempto	
dúbito		óccupo		voco	
erro		oppugno		volo	
exploro		opto		vúlnero	
exspecto		oro		sum	

Give Meanings:

cras		nunc	
heri		saepe	
hódie		semper	
non		tum	
numquam		umquam	

Latin Sayings:

In choro recitémus.	
Stabat Mater	
In umbra, ígitur, pugnábimus.	
Ora et labora.	
Errare est humanum.	
Civis Romanus sum.	
nunc aut numquam	
semper fidelis	
Fortes fortuna juvat.	

Answer the Grammar questions:

1. Verb families are called_____ .

2. Give the 6 attributes of a Latin verb._____

   _____

3. Give the three grammar persons. _____

4. Give the two grammar numbers. _____

5. The stem vowel of the 1st conjugation is _____ .

6. In English, *I praise* is the _____ present, *I am praising* is the _____ present,

   and *I do praise* is the_____ present.

7. The imperfect tense sign is _____ .

8. What English helping verbs translate the imperfect tense? _____

9. How many words are needed to make a Latin sentence?_____

10. The future tense sign is _____ .

11. What English helping verb translates the Latin future tense? _____

12. Name the 3 tenses that make up the Present System. _____

    _____

13. The forms that provide the stems needed to conjugate a verb in all its tenses are called the

    _____   _____ .

14. Give the regular endings for the principal parts of 1st conjugation verbs._____

    _____

15. What is the name of the 2nd principal part? _____

16. How do you find the present stem? _____

17. The English infinitive is written with the particle _____ before the verb.

18. The 'to be' verb shows _____ , not action.

19. Give the English forms of the 'to be' verb. _____

    _____

20. How do you find the perfect stem?_____

21. Give 3 translations for *vocavi.*_____

22. What English helping verbs translate the perfect tense?_____

23. What English helping verb translates the pluperfect tense?_____

24. What English helping verbs translate the future perfect tense?_____

25. Name the tenses that make up the Perfect System. _____

    _____

Translate from Latin to English:

1. nuntiávimus _____

2. volabat _____

3. speratis _____

4. navigabunt _____

5. láveras _____

6. laudaverunt _____

7. dedéritis _____

8. amabamus _____

9. paráverit _____

10. stetisti _____

Translate from English to Latin:

1. they were telling _____

2. I have washed _____

3. she will have explored _____

4. you (pl.) had greeted _____

5. we will attack _____

6. you stand _____

7. he has judged _____

8. they had overcome _____

9. I was fighting _____

10. we will have reported _____

Bonus:

1. Give the principal parts of *sum*. _____

2. Give the principal parts of *lavo*. _____

3. Give the principal parts of *sto*. _____

Vocabulary (give dictionary form, including gender):

earth, land	_____	table	_____
Italy	_____	Mary	_____
girl	_____	queen	_____
sailor	_____	poet	_____
Rome	_____	farmer	_____

A. Answer the following:

1. Does Latin have articles like English? _____

2. How many grammatical genders does Latin have? _____

3. Name them: _____

4. Gender that refers to male and female creatures is _____ gender.

5. What is the gender of most 1st declension nouns? _____

6. Which three nouns in the vocabulary for this lesson are masculine? _____

_____

7. If the genitive singular of a noun ends in _____ , it is a first declension noun.

B. Give the case names and the 1st declension case endings:

Case	Singular	Plural

C. Decline *terra* and give case names:

Case	Singular	Plural

D. Translate from Latin to English (nominative only):

1. poetae _____

2. regina _____

3. puellae _____

4. nauta _____

5. Itália _____

6. terrae _____

E. Translate from English to Latin (nominative only):

1. queens _____

2. sailors _____

3. poet _____

4. tables _____

5. Mary _____

6. girls _____

Latin Saying:

Eternal Rome _____

Bonus:

1. Give the articles in English: _____

Vocabulary (give dictionary form, including gender):

year	_____	Rome	_____
god	_____	horse	_____
earth, land	_____	table	_____
Italy	_____	Mary	_____
lamb	_____	lord, master	_____
girl	_____	queen	_____
friend	_____	world, mankind	_____
Christ	_____	poet	_____
sailor	_____	son	_____
slave, servant	_____	farmer	_____

A. Give the case names and endings for the 2nd declension *us* nouns:

Case	Singular	Plural

B. Answer the following:

1. A 2nd declension noun whose nominative singular ends in *us* is usually _____ .

2. The genitive singular ending of 2nd declension nouns is _____ .

3. The subject of a verb is in the _____ case.

C. Decline *amicus*:

Case	Singular	Plural
nominative		
genitive		
dative		
accusative		
ablative		

D. Translate from Latin to English (nominative only):

1. agni _____

2. equus _____

3. anni _____

4. mundus _____

5. amici _____

6. fílii _____

E. Translate from English to Latin (nominative only):

1. master _____

2. horses _____

3. servant _____

4. sons _____

5. years _____

6. world _____

Latin Saying:

In the year of our Lord _____

Bonus:

1. What case ending would you use to form a plural subject in the 1st declension? _____

2. What case ending would you use to form a plural subject in the 2nd declension *us*? _____

Vocabulary (give dictionary form, including gender):

town	_____	sky, heaven	_____
war	_____	sailor	_____
year	_____	slave, servant	_____
god	_____	Rome	_____
gift	_____	horse	_____
earth, land	_____	temple	_____
word	_____	table	_____
kingdom	_____	Mary	_____
Italy	_____	lord, master	_____
lamb	_____	queen	_____
rock	_____	debt, sin	_____
girl	_____	world, mankind	_____
forum, marketplace	_____	poet	_____
friend	_____	son	_____
Christ	_____	farmer	_____

A. Give the case names and endings for the 2nd declension *um* nouns:

Case	Singular	Plural

B. Answer the following:

1. What gender is a 2nd declension noun whose nominative singular ends in *um*? _____

2. Give the two parts of the rule for neuter nouns of all declensions:

   _____

   _____

3. The genitive singular ending of 2nd declension nouns is _____ .

C. Decline *verbum* and give case names:

Case	Singular	Plural

D. Translate from Latin to English (nominative only):

1. templum _____
2. saxa _____
3. caelum _____
4. verba _____
5. regnum _____
6. bella _____

E. Translate from English to Latin (nominative only):

1. gifts _____
2. forums _____
3. debt _____
4. towns _____
5. kingdoms _____
6. rock _____

Latin Saying:

before the war _____

Bonus:

1. Give the principal parts of *sum*: _____

_____

Vocabulary (give dictionary form, including gender):

town	_____	sky, heaven	_____
war	_____	sailor	_____
year	_____	slave, servant	_____
god	_____	Rome	_____
gift	_____	horse	_____
earth, land	_____	temple	_____
word	_____	table	_____
kingdom	_____	Mary	_____
Italy	_____	lord, master	_____
lamb	_____	queen	_____
rock	_____	debt, sin	_____
girl	_____	world, mankind	_____
forum, marketplace	_____	poet	_____
friend	_____	son	_____
Christ	_____	farmer	_____

A. Answer the following:

1. What case is used to classify nouns? _____

2. All nouns whose genitive singular ends in *ae* belong to the _____ declension.

3. All nouns whose genitive singular ends in *i* belong to the _____ declension.

Bonus:

1. A verb must agree with its subject in _____ and _____ .

B. Decline *regnum*:

Case	Singular	Plural
nominative		
genitive		
dative		
accusative		
ablative		

C. Decline *regina*:

Case	Singular	Plural
nominative		
genitive		
dative		
accusative		
ablative		

D. Decline *annus*:

Case	Singular	Plural
nominative		
genitive		
dative		
accusative		
ablative		

Vocabulary (give dictionary form):

small	_____	good	_____
bad	_____	great, large	_____
new	_____	eternal, everlasting	_____
much, many	_____	wide, broad	_____
sacred, holy	_____	high, deep	_____

A. Decline *novus*:

Case	Singular		
	Masculine	Feminine	Neuter
nominative			
genitive			
dative			
accusative			
ablative			

Case	Plural		
	Masculine	Feminine	Neuter
nominative			
genitive			
dative			
accusative			
ablative			

B. Answer the following:

1. An adjective must agree with its noun in _____ .

2. An adjective is a word that _____ .

C. Translate the following in the nominative:

1. large horse _____

2. small gift _____

3. good years_____

4. many friends _____

5. bad war _____

6. new towns_____

7. eternal world _____

8. many words _____

9. wide forum _____

10. good farmer _____

11. bad poets_____

12. wide tables _____

D. Translate:

1. The horse walks. _____

2. The horses walk. _____

3. The farmer was working. _____

4. The farmers were working. _____

Latin Saying:

   The mother of Italy, Rome _____

Bonus:

1. Adjectives of quantity or size usually _____ the noun.

2. Adjectives of quality usually _____ the noun.

Vocabulary (give dictionary form for 'one' and for the ordinals):

one	_____	first	_____
two	_____	second	_____
three	_____	third	_____
four	_____	fourth	_____
five	_____	fifth	_____
six	_____	sixth	_____
seven	_____	seventh	_____
eight	_____	eighth	_____
nine	_____	ninth	_____
ten	_____	tenth	_____

A. Give the cardinal and ordinal numbers in English:

1. 5 _____

2. 7 _____

3. 3 _____

4. 2 _____

B. Answer the following:

1. _____ numbers are counting numbers.

2. _____ numbers order things in a series.

3. A predicate adjective follows a _____ .

4. A predicate adjective describes the _____ .

5. A predicate adjective is in the _____ case.

6. A predicate nominative is a _____ following a _____ .

7. A predicate nominative _____ the subject.

8. A predicate nominative is always in the _____ case.

C. Decline *tertius*:

Case	Singular		
	Masculine	Feminine	Neuter
nominative			
genitive			
dative			
accusative			
ablative			

Case	Plural		
	Masculine	Feminine	Neuter
nominative			
genitive			
dative			
accusative			
ablative			

Latin Saying:

The four seasons of the year _____

Bonus:

Give the Roman numerals for the following numbers:

one _____   six _____

two _____   seven _____

three _____   eight _____

four _____   nine _____

five _____   ten _____

Vocabulary (give English meaning and *gender* of nouns):

magnus -a -um	_____	mundus -i	_____
agnus -i	_____	nauta -ae	_____
tres	_____	duo	_____
agrícola -ae	_____	óppidum -i	_____
aeternus -a -um	_____	poeta -ae	_____
amicus -i	_____	bonus -a -um	_____
quintus -a -um	_____	puella -ae	_____
annus -i	_____	regina -ae	_____
bellum -i	_____	latus -a -um	_____
septem	_____	regnum -i	_____
caelum -i	_____	octo	_____
décimus -a -um	_____	Roma -ae	_____
sanctus -a -um	_____	quartus -a -um	_____
Christus -i	_____	saxum -i	_____
débitum -i	_____	séptimus -a -um	_____
quinque	_____	servus -i	_____
deus -i	_____	altus -a -um	_____
dóminus -i	_____	templum -i	_____
primus -a -um	_____	sex	_____
donum -i	_____	terra -ae	_____
parvus -a -um	_____	quáttuor	_____
equus -i	_____	unus -a -um	_____
fílius -i	_____	verbum -i	_____
novus -a -um	_____	tértius -a -um	_____
forum -i	_____	malus -a -um	_____
Itália -ae	_____	sextus -a -um	_____
novem	_____	secundus -a -um	_____
Maria -ae	_____	decem	_____
mensa -ae	_____	multus -a -um	_____
nonus -a -um	_____	octavus -a -um	_____

Give the case endings for the 1st declension:

Case	Singular	Plural
nominative		
genitive		
dative		
accusative		
ablative		

Give the case endings for the 2nd declension *us*:

Case	Singular	Plural
nominative		
genitive		
dative		
accusative		
ablative		

Give the case endings for the 2nd declension *um*:

Case	Singular	Plural
nominative		
genitive		
dative		
accusative		
ablative		

Decline *parvus*:

Case	Singular		
	Masculine	Feminine	Neuter
nominative			
genitive			
dative			
accusative			
ablative			

Case	Plural		
	Masculine	Feminine	Neuter
nominative			
genitive			
dative			
accusative			
ablative			

Latin Sayings:

Roma Aeterna	
Anno Dómini	
Quattuor anni témpora	
ante bellum	
Mater Itáliae, Roma	

Grammar:

1. Verb families are called _____ and noun families are called _____ .

2. How many declensions are there? _____

3. Give the four attributes of nouns. _____

4. The three genders are _____ .

5. Nouns that name male and female persons have _____ gender.

6. Nouns that name non-living things have _____ gender.

7. First declension nouns are usually _____ in gender.

8. Three important exceptions to the 1st declension gender rule are _____

    _____ .

9. The genitive singular of the 1st declension is _____ .

10. The genitive singular of the 2nd declension is _____ .

11. Latin does not have the English articles _____ .

12. Second declension *us* nouns are usually _____ in gender.

13. Name the two subgroups of the 2nd declension, with their genders.

    1) _____

    2) _____

14. Verbs have tense and nouns have _____ endings.

15. Second declension *um* nouns are always _____ in gender.

16. The declension a noun belongs to is determined by the _____ case.

17. How do you find the stem of a Latin noun? _____

18. What is the subject case?_____ the direct object case?_____

    the indirect object case? _____ the possessive case? _____

    the *in/by/with/from* case?_____ the *to/for* case? _____

    the *of* case? _____ the predicate nominative case? _____

    the predicate adjective case? _____

19. Define adjective._____

20. In Latin an adjective must agree with its noun in _____ , _____ ,

and _____ , but not _____ .

21. Usually an adjective of _____ precedes a noun, and an adjective of

_____ follows the noun.

22. Counting numbers are called _____ .

23. Numbers which indicate the order of things in a series are called _____ .

24. Both kinds of numbers are what part of speech? _____

25. A sentence has two main parts: the _____ and the _____ .

26. A noun that follows a linking verb and renames the subject is a _____ .

27. An adjective that follows a linking verb and describes the subject is a _____

_____ .

28. Give the neuter rule: _____

_____

Translate:

1. The table is new. _____

2. Mary is a girl. _____

3. The towns were large. _____

4. The earth is good. _____

5. Marcus will be a sailor. _____

6. The words are eternal. _____

7. Marcus is a good friend. _____

8. The fourth lamb is small. _____

9. Five horses will be new. _____

10. Marcus is a new friend. _____

Bonus:

1. Latin is a language of _____ and _____ .

2. Always in Latin and usually in English, *c* is soft before _____ , _____ , _____ , and _____ .

3. Always in Latin and usually in English, *c* is hard before _____ , _____ , _____ , and consonants.

Vocabulary (give dictionary form):

sister   _____   mother   _____

soldier   _____   brother   _____

father   _____   leader   _____

king   _____

Latin Saying:

nurturing mother _____

A. Answer the following:

1. How do you find the stem of a 3rd declension noun? _____

_____

2. The genitive singular of a _____ declension noun ends in *is.*

3. The 3rd declension has nouns of_____ genders.

B. Give the case endings for masculine and feminine 3rd declension nouns:

Case	Singular	Plural
nominative		
genitive		
dative		
accusative		
ablative		

Bonus (Translate):

1. dux novus_____   3. sorores (good) _____

2. mílites magni _____   4. (small) mater _____

C. Decline *mater*:

Case	Singular	Plural
nominative		
genitive		
dative		
accusative		
ablative		

D. Decline *dux*:

Case	Singular	Plural
nominative		
genitive		
dative		
accusative		
ablative		

E. Translate from Latin to English (nominative only):

1. patres _____

2. miles _____

3. frater _____

4. matres _____

5. sorores _____

6. rex _____

F. Translate from English to Latin (nominative only):

1. sister _____

2. leaders _____

3. mother _____

4. soldiers _____

5. father _____

6. kings _____

Vocabulary (give dictionary form):

law   _____   king   _____

dog   _____   mother   _____

sister   _____   foot   _____

custom   _____   brother   _____

soldier   _____   bread   _____

peace   _____   leader   _____

father   _____   light   _____

cross   _____   voice   _____

sun   _____

A. Decline *lux*:

Case	Singular	Plural
nominative		
genitive		
dative		
accusative		
ablative		

B. Decline *canis*:

Case	Singular	Plural
nominative		
genitive		
dative		
accusative		
ablative		

C. Decline *pes*:

Case	Singular	Plural
nominative		
genitive		
dative		
accusative		
ablative		

D. Translate from Latin to English (nominative only):

1. panis _____

2. soles _____

3. vox _____

4. leges _____

5. mores _____

6. pes _____

E. Translate from English to Latin (nominative only):

1. voices _____

2. cross _____

3. dogs _____

4. peace _____

5. feet _____

6. sun _____

Latin Saying:

The Roman Peace _____

Bonus:

1. Explain why *canis* can be either masculine or feminine. _____

_____

_____

Vocabulary (give dictionary form):

river	_____	sun	_____
law	_____	king	_____
dog	_____	head	_____
sister	_____	mother	_____
custom	_____	foot	_____
lamp	_____	brother	_____
soldier	_____	bread	_____
peace	_____	leader	_____
name	_____	light	_____
father	_____	heart	_____
cross	_____	voice	_____

A. Answer the following:

1. Give the two parts of the neuter rule._____

_____

_____

2. How do you find the stem of a 3rd declension noun? _____

_____

B. Decline *lumen*:

Case	Singular	Plural
nominative		
genitive		
dative		
accusative		
ablative		

C. Decline *caput*:

Case	Singular	Plural
nominative		
genitive		
dative		
accusative		
ablative		

D. Translate from Latin to English (nominative only):

1. lumen _____

2. corda _____

3. nomen _____

4. flúmina _____

5. caput _____

E. Translate from English to Latin (nominative only):

1. heart _____

2. names _____

3. heads _____

4. lamps _____

5. river _____

Latin Saying:

Caput Mundi _____

Bonus (Translate):

1. many rivers_____

2. new name _____

3. magna cápita _____

4. cor sanctum _____

Vocabulary (give dictionary form):

peace	_____	king	_____
lamp	_____	custom	_____
bread	_____	cross	_____
head	_____	foot	_____
mother	_____	leader	_____
voice	_____	name	_____
sister	_____	law	_____
soldier	_____	sun	_____
river	_____	light	_____
brother	_____	dog	_____
heart	_____	father	_____

Latin Saying:

King of Kings _____

A. Answer the following:

1. The noun that follows a linking verb and renames the subject is a _____, not a direct object.

2. The direct object of a verb is in the _____ case.

B. Decline *rex*:

Case	Singular	Plural
nominative		
genitive		
dative		
accusative		
ablative		

C. Decline *flumen*:

Case	Singular	Plural
nominative		
genitive		
dative		
accusative		
ablative		

D. Decline *pax*:

Case	Singular	Plural
nominative		
genitive		
dative		
accusative		
ablative		

E. Translate from Latin to English (nominative only):

1. sorores _____
2. flúmina _____
3. canis _____
4. duces _____
5. mos _____
6. mílites _____

F. Translate from English to Latin (nominative only):

1. lamps _____
2. brothers _____
3. heart _____
4. heads _____
5. bread _____
6. dogs _____

Bonus:

1. Give the four attributes of nouns. _____

Vocabulary (give dictionary form):

fruit	_____	spirit	_____
senate	_____	harbor	_____
arrival	_____	hand	_____
fear	_____	lake	_____
house	_____	army	_____

A. Answer the following:

1. The genitive singular of all 4th declension nouns ends in _____ .

2. Most 4th declension nouns are of the _____ gender.

B. Decline *manus*:

Case	Singular	Plural
nominative		
genitive		
dative		
accusative		
ablative		

C. Decline *domus*:

Case	Singular	Plural
nominative		
genitive		
dative		
accusative		
ablative		

D. Translate from Latin to English (nominative only):

1. exércitus _____

2. portūs _____

3. adventus _____

4. lacūs _____

5. domūs _____

6. spíritus _____

E. Translate from English to Latin (nominative only):

1. hands _____

2. fruit _____

3. fears _____

4. senate _____

5. armies _____

6. house _____

Latin Saying:

The Senate and People of Rome _____

_____

Bonus (translate):

1. Reginam spectavit. _____

2. The son had shouted the words. _____

Vocabulary (give dictionary form):

day _____   face _____

senate _____   harbor _____

faith, trust _____   hand _____

arrival _____   thing, matter, affair, business _____

fear _____   hope _____

house _____   lake _____

spirit _____   army _____

fruit _____

Latin Saying:

Seize the day. _____

A. Answer the following:

1. The genitive singular of all 5th declension nouns ends in _____ .

2. Most 5th declension nouns are of the _____ gender.

B. Decline *dies*:

Case	Singular	Plural
nominative		
genitive		
dative		
accusative		
ablative		

Bonus (translate):

1. Hope had changed the spirit._____

Name_____ Date _____

Vocabulary. Give dictionary form:

custom _____   law _____

harbor _____   peace _____

heart _____   head _____

fruit _____   hope _____

dog _____   river _____

brother _____   lamp _____

king _____   foot _____

father _____   spirit _____

fear _____   army _____

day _____   house, home _____

lake _____   bread _____

thing, matter _____   light _____

leader _____   cross _____

hand _____   sun _____

voice _____   arrival _____

sister _____   mother _____

face _____   name _____

senate _____   soldier _____

faith, trust _____   fear _____

Latin Sayings:

1. The Roman Peace _____

2. Head of the World _____

3. Seize the day. _____

4. nurturing mother _____

5. King of Kings _____

6. The Senate and the People of Rome _____

A. Declensions: Write the names of the cases and decline *panis*

Case	Singular	Plural

B. Decline: *miles* and *cor*

Singular	Plural	Singular	Plural
miles		cor	

C. Decline: *manus* and *fides*

Singular	Plural	Singular	Plural
manus		fides	

A. Vocabulary (Complete dictionary form and give English meaning):

1. adventus _____
2. aeternus _____
3. agnus _____
4. agrícola _____
5. altus _____
6. amicus _____
7. annus _____
8. bellum _____
9. bonus _____
10. caelum _____
11. canis _____
12. caput _____
13. Christus _____
14. cor _____
15. crux _____
16. débitum _____
17. deus _____
18. dies _____
19. dóminus _____
20. domus _____
21. donum _____
22. dux _____
23. equus _____
24. exércitus _____
25. fácies _____
26. fides _____
27. fílius _____
28. flumen _____
29. forum _____
30. frater _____
31. fructus _____
32. Itália _____
33. lacus _____
34. latus _____
35. lex _____
36. lumen _____
37. lux _____
38. magnus _____
39. malus _____

40. manus _____
41. Maria _____
42. mater _____
43. mensa _____
44. metus _____
45. miles _____
46. mos _____
47. multus _____
48. mundus _____
49. nauta _____
50. nomen _____
51. novus _____
52. óppidum _____
53. panis _____
54. parvus _____
55. pater _____
56. pax _____
57. pes _____
58. poeta _____
59. portus _____
60. puella _____
61. regina _____
62. regnum _____
63. res _____
64. rex _____
65. Roma _____
66. sanctus _____
67. saxum _____
68. senatus _____
69. servus _____
70. sol _____
71. soror _____
72. spes _____
73. spíritus _____
74. templum _____
75. terra _____
76. verbum _____
77. vox _____

B. Decline *res*:

Case	Singular	Plural
nominative		
genitive		
dative		
accusative		
ablative		

C. Decline *portus*:

Case	Singular	Plural
nominative		
genitive		
dative		
accusative		
ablative		

D. Decline *equus*:

Case	Singular	Plural
nominative		
genitive		
dative		
accusative		
ablative		

E. Decline *vox*:

Case	Singular	Plural
nominative		
genitive		
dative		
accusative		
ablative		

F. Decline *nomen*:

Case	Singular	Plural
nominative		
genitive		
dative		
accusative		
ablative		

G. Decline *regnum*:

Case	Singular	Plural
nominative		
genitive		
dative		
accusative		
ablative		

H. Decline *puella*:

Case	Singular	Plural
nominative		
genitive		
dative		
accusative		
ablative		

I. Latin Sayings:

1. The Roman Peace _____

2. Head of the World _____

3. Seize the day. _____

4. nurturing mother _____

5. King of Kings _____

6. The Senate and the People of Rome _____

J. Translate:

1. many rocks _____

2. good faith _____

3. good bread _____

4. wide harbor _____

5. four feet _____

6. fourth sailor _____

7. new tables _____

Bonus (translate):

1. Hope had changed the spirit. _____

2. The sons will have blamed the master. _____

K. Grammar:

1. Verb families are called _____ and noun families are
    called _____ .
2. How many declensions are there? _____
3. Give the four attributes of nouns. _____
4. The three genders are _____ .
5. Nouns that name male and female persons have_____ gender.
6. Nouns that name non-living things have _____ gender.
7. First declension nouns are usually _____ in gender.
8. The genitive singular of the 1st declension is _____ .
9. The genitive singular of the 2nd declension is _____ .
10. Second declension *us* nouns are usually _____ in gender.
11. Second declension *um* nouns are always _____ in gender.
12. The declension a noun belongs to is determined by the _____ case.
13. How do you find the stem of a Latin noun? _____
14. What is the subject case?_____ the direct object case?_____
    the indirect object case? _____ the possessive case? _____
    the *in/by/with/from* case?_____ the *to/for* case? _____ the *of*
    case?_____ the predicate nominative case?_____ the
    predicate adjective case?_____
15. In Latin an adjective must agree with its noun in _____, _____,
    and _____ , but not _____ .
16. Counting numbers are called _____ .
17. Numbers which indicate the order of things in a series are called _____ .
18. Both kinds of numbers are what part of speech? _____
19. A sentence has two main parts: the _____ and the _____ .
20. A noun that follows a linking verb and renames the subject is a _____ .
21. An adjective that follows a linking verb and describes the subject is a _____ .
22. Give the neuter rule: _____

    _____
23. The genitive singular of the 3rd declension is _____ .
24. How can you know the gender of a 3rd declension noun?_____

    _____
25. What kind of verb is never followed by a direct object? _____
26. The genitive singular of the 4th declension is_____ .
27. The genitive singular of the 5th declension is _____ .
28. Most 4th declension nouns are _____ in gender, and most 5th declension
    nouns are _____ in gender.

Vocabulary: Give the infinitive form for each Latin verb.

to warn	_____	to move	_____
to owe	_____	to hold	_____
to see	_____	to teach	_____
to sit	_____	to have	_____
to rejoice	_____	to be silent	_____

A. Answer the following:

1. The infinitive of 2nd conjugation verbs ends in _____ .

2. How do you find the stem of a 2nd conjugation verb? _____

_____

3. The stem vowel of the 2nd conjugation is _____ .

B. Conjugate *móneo* in the present tense:

Person	Singular	Meaning	Plural	Meaning
1st				
2nd				
3rd				

C. Conjugate *sédeo* in the present tense:

Person	Singular	Meaning	Plural	Meaning
1st				
2nd				
3rd				

D. Translate from Latin to English:

1. moves _____

2. docent _____

3. gáudeo _____

4. debet _____

5. tacetis _____

6. videmus _____

E. Translate from English to Latin:

1. you (pl.) sit _____

2. we are silent _____

3. I hold _____

4. they have _____

5. you see _____

6. it moves _____

F. Translate:

1. We ought to be silent. _____

2. I ought to sit. _____

Latin Saying:

I see and am silent. _____

Bonus (translate):

1. The queen has big feet. _____

2. Nautae latum flumen vident. _____

Vocabulary (give dictionary form):

to prevent	_____	to appear	_____
to frighten	_____	to move	_____
to warn	_____	to hold	_____
to owe, ought	_____	to order, command	_____
to beware of, guard against	_____	to be strong, be well	_____
		to teach	_____
to see	_____	to have	_____
to fear, be afraid of	_____	to burn, be on fire	_____
to respond, answer	_____	to be silent	_____
to sit	_____	to remain, stay	_____
to rejoice	_____		

A. Conjugate *máneo* in the imperfect tense:

Person	Singular	Meaning	Plural	Meaning
1st				
2nd				
3rd				

B. Conjugate *júbeo* in the future tense:

Person	Singular	Meaning	Plural	Meaning
1st				
2nd				
3rd				

C. Conjugate *tímeo* in the present system:

Person	Present		Imperfect	
1st				
2nd				
3rd				

Person	Future	
1st		
2nd		
3rd		

D. Translate from Latin to English:

1. terrebit _____

2. prohibebam _____

3. valebant _____

4. manebis _____

5. ardebat _____

6. jubebam_____

7. cavebamus _____

8. prohibebit _____

E. Translate from English to Latin:

1. we were well _____

2. I will respond _____

3. it will appear _____

4. they will prevent _____

5. she was ordering _____

6. you were fearing _____

7. they were bewaring of _____

8. you (pl.) will remain _____

Latin Saying:

Beware the dog. _____

Bonus (translate):

1. The bad poet was afraid of big words._____

A. Give the principal parts for the following verbs:

1st	2nd	3rd	4th
hábeo			
táceo			
móneo			
débeo			
appáreo			
prohíbeo			
térreo			

B. Give the principal parts for the following verbs:

1st	2nd	3rd	4th
dóceo			
téneo			
júbeo			
tímeo			
váleo			
máneo			
árdeo			

Latin Saying:

To teach, to delight, to move _____

Bonus (translate):

1. The small kingdom has many rivers. _____

A. Give the principal parts for the following verbs:

1st	2nd	3rd	4th
vídeo			
móveo			
gáudeo			
respóndeo			
sédeo			
cáveo			

B. Answer the following:

1. What are the tenses of the perfect system? _____

2. How do you form the tenses of the perfect system? _____

_____

3. How do you find the perfect stem? _____

_____

C. Translate from Latin to English:

1. sedistis _____

2. docúerat _____

3. jússerint _____

4. responderunt _____

5. móveras _____

6. tenúimus _____

7. prohibueratis _____

8. vidi _____

D. Conjugate *vídeo* in the perfect system:

P	Perfect		Pluperfect	
1st				
2nd				
3rd				

P	Future Perfect	
1st		
2nd		
3rd		

E. Translate from English to Latin:

1. we had seen _____

2. they will have responded _____

3. you (pl.) have held _____

4. I had taught _____

5. she has remained _____

6. you will have warned _____

7. he has moved _____

8. they have ordered _____

Latin Saying:

I came, I saw, I conquered. _____

Bonus (translate):

1. Good soldiers were preventing a great fear. _____

_____

Vocabulary: Give the infinitive form for each Latin verb.

to prevent	_____	to appear	_____
to frighten	_____	to move	_____
to warn	_____	to hold	_____
to owe, ought	_____	to order, command	_____
to beware of	_____	to be well, be strong	_____
to see	_____	to teach	_____
to fear, be afraid of	_____	to have	_____
to respond, answer	_____	to burn, be on fire	_____
to sit	_____	to be silent	_____
to rejoice	_____	to remain, stay	_____

A. Conjugate *débeo* in the present system:

Person	Present		Imperfect	
1st				
2nd				
3rd				

Person	Future	
1st		
2nd		
3rd		

B. Conjugate *débeo* in the perfect system:

P	Perfect		Pluperfect	
1st				
2nd				
3rd				

P	Future Perfect	
1st		
2nd		
3rd		

C. Latin Sayings:

1. Beware the dog. _____

2. I see and am silent. _____

3. To teach, to delight, to move _____

4. I came, I saw, I conquered. _____

Principal parts:

1. to rejoice _____

2. to order, command _____

3. to beware of, guard against _____

4. to sit _____

5. to have _____

6. to move _____

7. to hold _____

8. to fear, be afraid of_____

A. Conjugate *amo* in the present and perfect systems with meanings:

present stem_____   meanings

Present	

Present	

Imperfect	

Imperfect	

Future	

Future	

perfect stem_____   meanings

Perfect	

Perfect	

Pluperfect	

Pluperfect	

Future Perfect	

Future Perfect	

B. Conjugate *móneo* and *sum* in the present and perfect systems.

present stem_____

Sum does not have a present stem.

Present	
móneo	

Present	
sum	

Imperfect	

Imperfect	

Future	

Future	

perfect stem_____

perfect stem_____

Perfect	

Perfect	

Pluperfect	

Pluperfect	

Future Perfect	

Future Perfect	

C. Fifty 1st conjugation verbs. Give dictionary form:

English	Latin	English	Latin
1. to accuse		26. to judge, consider	
2. to address		27. to live in, dwell	
3. to adore		28. to look at	
4. to ask		29. to love, like	
5. to attack		30. to overcome	
6. to blame		31. to plow	
7. to call		32. to praise	
8. to carry		33. to prepare	
9. to change		34. to report	
10. to create		35. to sail	
11. to delight, please		36. to seize	
12. to deny		37. to set free	
13. to desire, wish		38. to shout	
14. to disturb		39. to show, point out	
15. to doubt		40. to speak, pray	
16. to err, wander		41. to stand	
17. to explore		42. to swim	
18. to fight		43. to tell	
19. to fly		44. to tempt	
20. to give		45. to think	
21. to greet		46. to wait for, expect	
22. to guard, keep		47. to walk	
23. to help		48. to wash	
24. to hide		49. to work	
25. to hope		50. to wound	

D. Twenty 2nd conjugation verbs. Give all principal parts:

1st	2nd	3rd	4th	Meaning
móneo				
appáreo				
débeo				
hábeo				
prohíbeo				
térreo				
táceo				
tímeo				
váleo				
dóceo				
téneo				
árdeo				
júbeo				
máneo				
gáudeo				
cáveo				
sédeo				
vídeo				
respóndeo				
móveo				

E. 1st Conjugation principal parts and *sum:*

1. to love _____

2. to carry _____

3. to give _____

4. to stand _____

5. to wash _____

6. to help _____

7. to be _____

F. Latin Sayings:

1. Beware the dog _____

2. I see and am silent. _____

3. To teach, to delight, to move _____

4. I came, I saw, I conquered. _____

5. Let us recite together. _____

6. The Mother was Standing _____

7. Then we will fight in the shade. _____

8. I am a Roman citizen. _____

9. To err is human._____

10. now or never _____

11. always faithful_____

12. Fortune aids the brave. _____

13. Pray and work. _____

A. Conjugate *amo* in 6 tenses:

Person	Present		Imperfect	
1st				
2nd				
3rd				

Person	Future		Perfect	
1st				
2nd				
3rd				

Person	Pluperfect		Future Perfect	
1st				
2nd				
3rd				

B. Conjugate *móneo* in 6 tenses:

Person	Present		Imperfect	
1st				
2nd				
3rd				

Person	Future		Perfect	
1st				
2nd				
3rd				

Person	Pluperfect		Future Perfect	
1st				
2nd				
3rd				

C. Decline the model nouns (Put the case names for the 1st declension):

Case	Singular	Plural
	mensa	

Singular	Plural	Singular	Plural
servus		bellum	

Singular	Plural	Singular	Plural
pater		nomen	

Singular	Plural	Singular	Plural
portus		res	

D. Form Drill (English to Latin):

1. house (acc.) _____

2. queens (nom.)_____

3. heads (acc.) _____

4. brother (nom.) _____

5. poets (nom.) _____

6. lambs (nom.)_____

7. many words (nom.)_____

8. great farmer (nom.) _____

9. deep rivers (nom.) _____

10. bad name (nom.)_____

E. Latin to English (nominative case):

1. dei _____

2. fílii _____

3. flumen _____

4. patres _____

5. agrícolae _____

6. bella _____

7. corda magna_____

8. forum novum _____

9. alta flúmina_____

10. bona capita _____

F. Translate:

1. Mílites spem laudaverunt. _____

2. Sol lucem dedit. _____

3. Christus fidem dat. _____

4. Decem domūs tum ardebant. _____

5. Latum flumen parvos equos terrebit. _____

6. I was being silent. _____

7. You were moving. _____

8. The bad poet was afraid of big words. _____

9. The large town is now on fire. _____

10. The small kingdom has many rivers. _____

G. Latin Sayings:

1. alma mater _____

2. Anno Dómini (A.D.) _____

3. ante bellum _____

4. Caput Mundi _____

5. Carpe diem. _____

6. Cave canem. _____

7. Civis Romanus sum. _____

8. Docēre, delectare, movēre _____

9. Errare est humanum. _____

10. Fortes fortuna juvat. _____

11. In choro recitémus. _____

12. In umbra, ígitur, pugnábimus. _____

13. Mater Itáliae Roma _____

14. nunc aut numquam _____

15. Ora et labora. _____

16. Pax Romana _____

17. Quáttuor anni tempora _____

18. Rex Regum _____

19. Roma Aeterna _____

20. semper fidelis _____

21. Senatus Populúsque Romanus (SPQR) _____

22. Stabat Mater _____

23. Veni, vidi, vici. _____

24. Vídeo et táceo. _____

H. Vocabulary (give dictionary form):

to accuse	_____	eight	_____
to address	_____	eighth	_____
to adore	_____	to err, wander	_____
always	_____	eternal	_____
to appear	_____	ever	_____
army	_____	to explore	_____
arrival	_____	face	_____
to ask	_____	faith, trust	_____
to attack	_____	farmer	_____
bad	_____	father	_____
to be	_____	fear	_____
to be on fire, burn	_____	to fear, be afraid of	_____
to be silent	_____	fifth	_____
to be well, be strong	_____	to fight	_____
to beware of, guard against	_____	first	_____
to blame	_____	five	_____
bread	_____	to fly	_____
brother	_____	foot	_____
to call	_____	forum, marketplace	_____
to carry	_____	four	_____
to change	_____	fourth	_____
Christ	_____	friend	_____
to create	_____	to frighten	_____
cross	_____	fruit	_____
custom	_____	gift	_____
day	_____	girl	_____
debt, sin	_____	to give	_____
to delight, please	_____	god	_____
to deny	_____	good	_____
to desire, wish	_____	great, large	_____
to disturb	_____	to greet	_____
dog	_____	to guard, keep	_____
to doubt	_____	hand	_____
earth, land	_____	harbor	_____
		to have	_____

head	_____	to order, command	_____
heart	_____	to overcome, surpass	_____
to help	_____	to owe, ought	_____
to hide	_____	peace	_____
high, deep	_____	to plow	_____
to hold	_____	poet	_____
hope	_____	to praise	_____
to hope	_____	to prepare	_____
horse	_____	to prevent	_____
house, home	_____	queen	_____
Italy	_____	to rejoice	_____
to judge, consider	_____	to remain, stay	_____
king	_____	to report	_____
kingdom	_____	to respond, answer	_____
lake	_____	river	_____
lamb	_____	rock	_____
lamp	_____	Rome	_____
law	_____	sacred, holy	_____
leader	_____	to sail	_____
light	_____	sailor	_____
to live in, dwell	_____	second	_____
to look at	_____	to see	_____
lord, master	_____	to seize	_____
to love, like	_____	senate	_____
Mary	_____	to set free	_____
mother	_____	seven	_____
to move	_____	seventh	_____
much, many	_____	to shout	_____
name	_____	to show, point out	_____
never	_____	sister	_____
new	_____	to sit	_____
nine	_____	six	_____
ninth	_____	sixth	_____
not	_____	sky, heaven	_____
now	_____	slave, servant	_____
often	_____	small	_____
one	_____	soldier	_____

son   _____

to speak, pray   _____

spirit   _____   **Bonus:**

to stand   _____

sun   _____   1. Give the neuter rule. _____

to swim   _____   _____

table   _____   _____

to teach   _____   _____

to tell   _____   _____

temple   _____   _____

to tempt   _____   _____

ten   _____

tenth   _____   2. Define a predicate nominative.

then, at that time _____   _____

thing, matter, affair, business _____   _____

to think   _____   _____

third   _____   _____

three   _____   _____

today   _____

tomorrow   _____   3. Which noun case is used to classify a noun?

town   _____   _____

two   _____   Why? _____

voice   _____   _____

to wait for, expect_____   _____

to walk   _____

war   _____

to warn   _____

to wash   _____

wide, broad   _____

word   _____

to work   _____

world, mankind_____

to wound   _____

year   _____

yesterday   _____